A Gift for Giraffe

by Pamela Chanko
illustrated by Doug Jones

SCHOLASTIC INC.
New York • Toronto • London • Auckland • Sydney
Mexico City • New Delhi • Hong Kong • Buenos Aires

Designed by Maria Lilja
ISBN-13: 978-0-545-08852-7 • ISBN-10: 0-545-08852-6

First printing, January 2009

12 11 10 9 8 7 6 5 4 3 2 1 9 10 11 12 13 14/0

Building Vocabulary With This Book

This book contains eight key words that are important for all children to know. Read the story straight through for enjoyment. Then read it again, pausing to define and discuss each key word. Follow-up the tale with the fun activities on pages 14–16. When you're done, celebrate—kids will have added eight great words to their vocabularies!

Giraffe was very happy,
and he hummed a little tune.
"My birthday's in a week," he sang,
"and that is very soon!"

He hunted for his present.
"I just can't wait!" he said.
He finally found a package
underneath his mother's bed.

Giraffe picked up the package
and he wondered, "What's inside?"
It wasn't very tall,
and it wasn't very **wide**.

KEY WORD: **ruler**

Simple Definition: a long, flat stick used for measuring

Sample Sentence: We used a *ruler* to see how tall our plant had grown.

He could not see inside the box,
but he knew just what to do.
He said, "I'll use my **ruler**.
It will help me find a clue."

KEY WORD: inch

Simple Definition: a unit of length equal to 1/12 of a foot

Sample Sentence: A grasshopper can grow to be one *inch* long.

One side was six **inches** long,
the other side was eight.
Whatever was inside the box,
it couldn't be that great.

KEY WORD: **measure**

Simple Definition: to find out the size, weight, or amount of something

Sample Sentence: When you are cooking, you must *measure* carefully.

"I'll **measure** it again," he said,
"just to double check.
A present can't be good
if it's shorter than my neck!"

Giraffe was sad, but then he thought,
"There's something I forgot!
My gift could still be special
if its **weight** is quite a lot."

KEY WORD: **scale**

Simple Definition: a device used for weighing things

Sample Sentence: The doctor asked me to step on the *scale* so she could see my weight.

He put the package on a **scale**
and hoped with all his might.
But he was very sad to see
his birthday gift was light.

KEY WORD: **huge**

Simple Definition: extremely large

Sample Sentence: Most dinosaurs were *huge* animals.

Unhappily, he put the present
back beneath the bed.
He had wanted something **huge**,
but this was something small instead.

At last it was his birthday,
and his mother yelled, "Surprise!"
Giraffe looked sadly at his gift,
which hadn't changed in size.

KEY WORD: **mile**

Simple Definition: a unit of length equal to 5,280 feet

Sample Sentence: I ride the bus because my school is more than one *mile* away from my house.

Then Mother said, "Unwrap it!"
and Giraffe began to smile.
Inside there was a handmade scarf,
which went on for a **mile**!

Giraffe said, "What a special gift!
How beautiful! How nice!
Plus, it's longer than my neck.
I can wrap it more than twice!"

Meaning Match

measurement words

Listen to the definition. Then go to the WORD CHEST and find a vocabulary word that matches it.

1. extremely large
2. a long, flat stick used for measuring
3. how heavy something is
4. the size of something from side to side
5. a unit of length equal to 5,280 feet
6. a unit of length equal to 1/12 of a foot
7. to find out the size, weight, or amount of something
8. a device used for weighing things

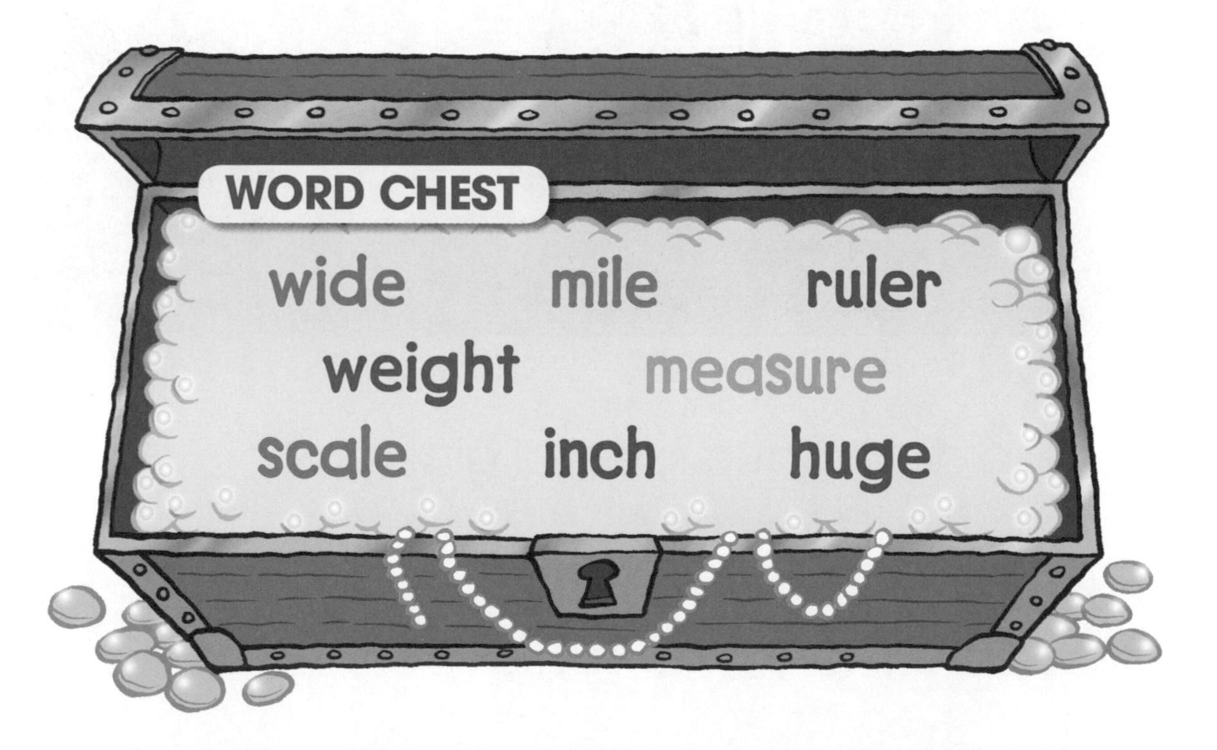

Answers: 1. huge 2. ruler 3. weight 4. wide 5. mile 6. inch 7. measure 8. scale

Vocabulary Fill-ins

measurement words

Listen to the sentence. Then go to the WORD BOX and find the best word to fill in the blank.

WORD BOX

weight	**scale**	**huge**	**ruler**
inch	**mile**	**measure**	**wide**

1. The hippo at the zoo was __________.
2. The table was __________ enough for two people to sit at each end.
3. Wow, the __________ of a blue whale is more than 20 elephants!
4. Put each pumpkin on the __________ to see which one is heavier.
5. Leo used a __________ to see how long the poster was.
6. We had to __________ the desk to see if it would fit in my room.
7. Samantha is only one __________ taller than Jillian.
8. We can walk to the mall because it is less than one __________ away.

Answers: 1. huge 2. wide 3. weight 4. scale 5. ruler 6. measure 7. inch 8. mile

Vocabulary Questions

measurement words

Listen to each question. Think about it. Then answer.

1. When was the last time you used a **scale**? How did it help you?
2. What is something in your home that is **wide**?
3. Does your doctor **measure** you when you go for a check-up? Why do you think this is done?
4. What is something you would like to have a **huge** amount of?
5. Imagine you are only one **inch** tall. What special things could you do that you can't do now?
6. The **weight** of an elephant is about 10,000 pounds! Would you like to be that heavy? Why or why not?
7. What are some things you can measure with a **ruler**? Make a list.
8. Do you think a **mile** is far or not far? Tell why you think so.

Extra: Can you think of some more measurement words? Make a list.